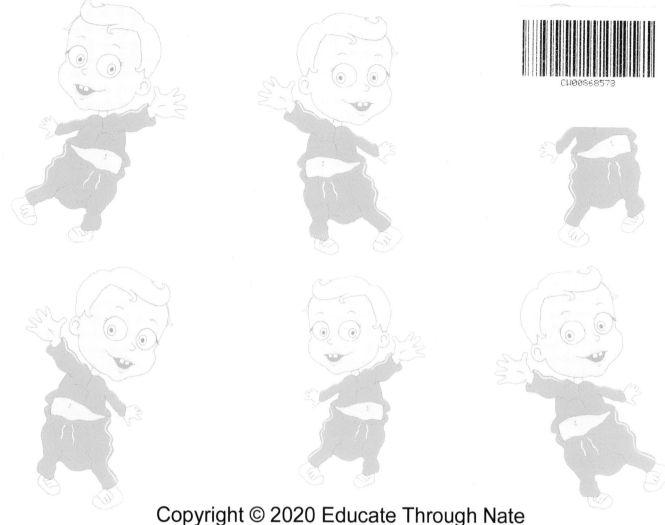

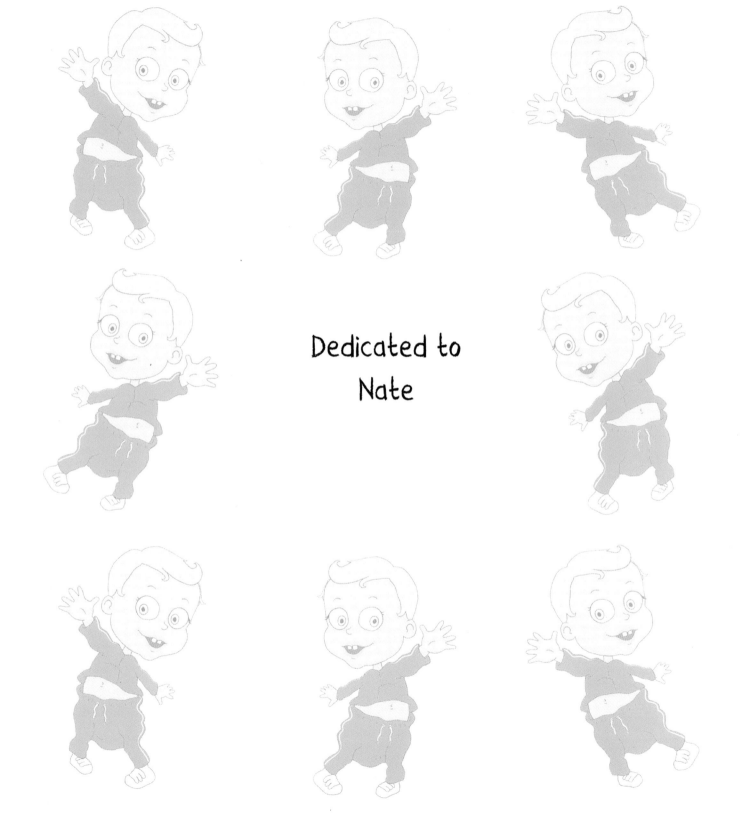

Dedicated to
Nate

Hello out there
my name is Nate,
and a very good day
to you.

Meet my Daddy, number '1'
and Daddy, number '2'.

"TWO DADDIES!" I hear you ask yourself.
"However can that be?"

Well, let me tell you all about
my special family!

When Daddy '1' met Daddy '2'
the air was filled with love.
They knew it had been sent to them
from somewhere high above.

They made a life together
and built a forever home.

But both of them were missing,
a baby of their own.

But, how can boys, just love boys,
and some girls love girls too?
love doesn't have a 'rule book' that
tells you what to do.

So they started a special journey,
and around the world they went.
Because they knew from high above
a baby would be sent.

So, meet my lady, number '1'
who gave the egg, that's me.
And then my lady, number '2'
who carried the pregnancy.

My name is Nate,
and by a twist of fate,
and a magical sprinkle of love.

I am part of this wonderful family,
a blessing from above.

I hope you like my story,
I can't wait to tell you more.

The excitement and adventure,
and the fun I have in store!

GOOD NIGHT

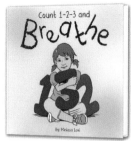

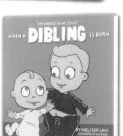
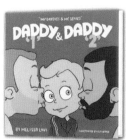
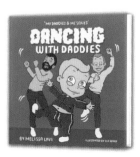
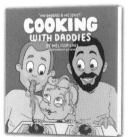

Printed in Great Britain
by Amazon